Slow and Steady Wins the Race

Written and Illustrated By
Reginald P. Howard

 Infinite Generations Publishing

Produced and Published by Infinite Generations
137 National Plaza, Suite 300
National Harbor, MD 20745
www.infinitegenerations.com

ISBN:
978-1-953364-60-9 (Paperback)

Dear Readers:

Thank you for your purchase.
I hope you enjoy Reggie: Slow and Steady Wins the Race.

Please share a review of this book on Amazon.

Visit my website for discounts, contests, and/or giveaways.
www.reginaldphoward.com

Follow Reginald Howard:
instagram.com/artby_reginaldhoward
www.facebook.com/reggiephoward/

This book, alongside others produced, were created with the sole intent to cause laughter and bring smiles to the reader. I'm hoping they'll reflect on their own family funny story as they do. I'm pretty sure, all families have relatable tales similar to my collection of stories.

Focusing on a few family, friends, and an occasional new reader, the book's true value increases with every laugh. Sure, chasing 'Best Seller' goals are nice for the astute author, but for me, I tend to focus on what's truly important; and that is having my stories and my art joyfully impact the reader for a good chuckle or two.

$\mathcal{B}$aseball is America's
favorite pastime. It was
our favorite pastime too,
once we learned the game.

$\mathcal{W}$e all can relate to the dreaded rope climb in P.E. class. It was actually pretty easy to do when you knew the proper techniques for climbing a rope. The hard part was getting down, especially after fatigue set in.

Reginald P. Howard

$\mathcal{D}$ad, there's a mouse in the house! "Oh no!" said Dad, "we gotta get him before Nonie sees him!" The mouse was clever, very difficult to find. Finally, after being very patient and persistent, the mouse reared his ugly little head.

When I reach him, and he darts out,
you whack him with that shoe.....

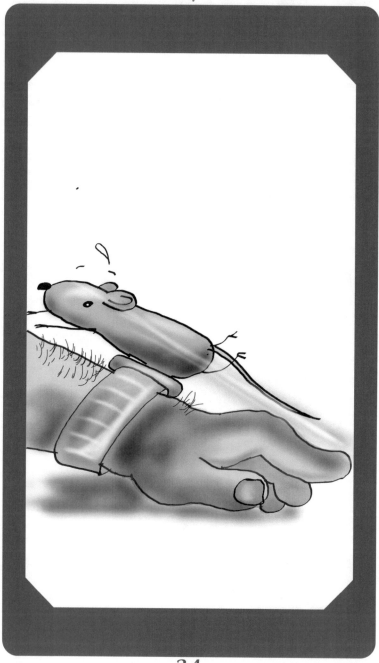

Sometimes I'd catch bugs just for kicks. No matter the size, I still wanted to catch them. Standing very still, and steady, I pounced on the ultimate prize one day- a Praying Mantis!

Dangit....Got away...

$\mathcal{D}$ad hated the sound of popping gum, especially when popped directly in his ear. And note to self: never pop it while he's watching a ball game.

47

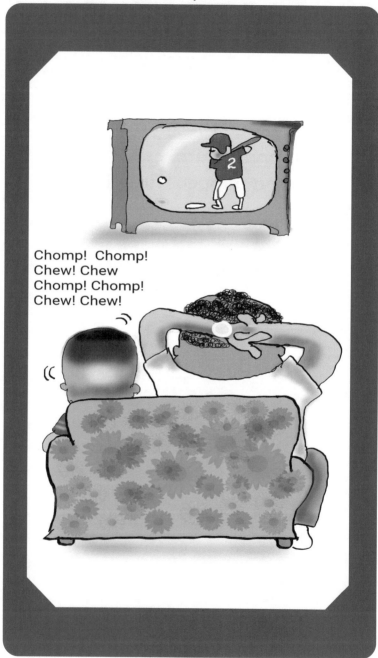

49

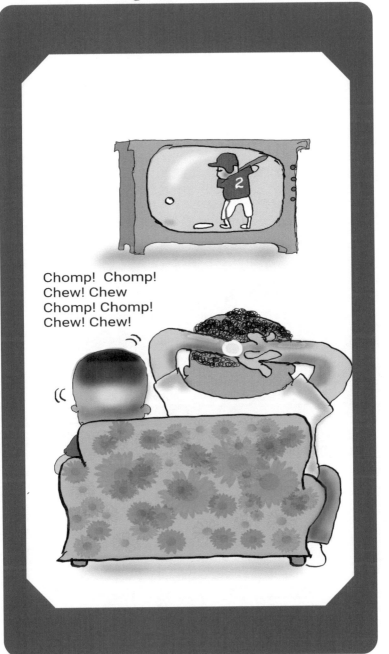

*E*very child has an accident
every once in a while.   But
Stephanie seemed to have
horrific accidents ALL the
time!

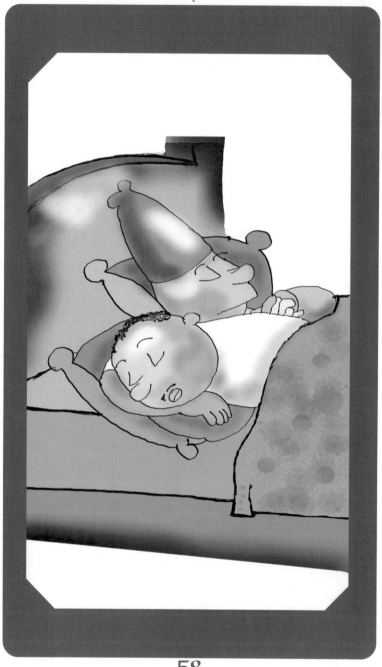

Dad hated homework hour. Even more, he hated the fact that his instructions weren't sinking in. It was frustrating to see the lessons roll off us like water off a duck's back. Slow and steady was not working for him.

Let me phrase the
question differently.....

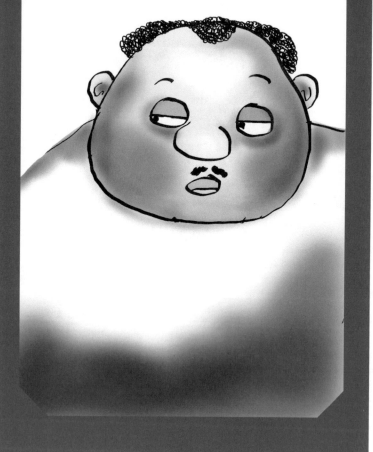

What's one belt, plus one belt?

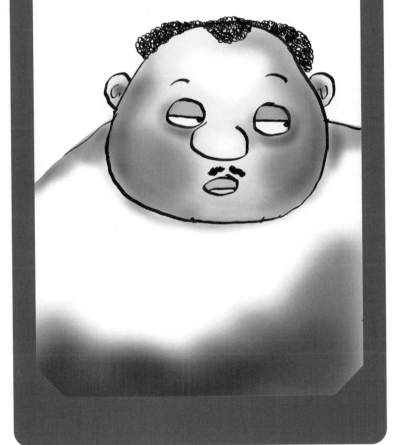

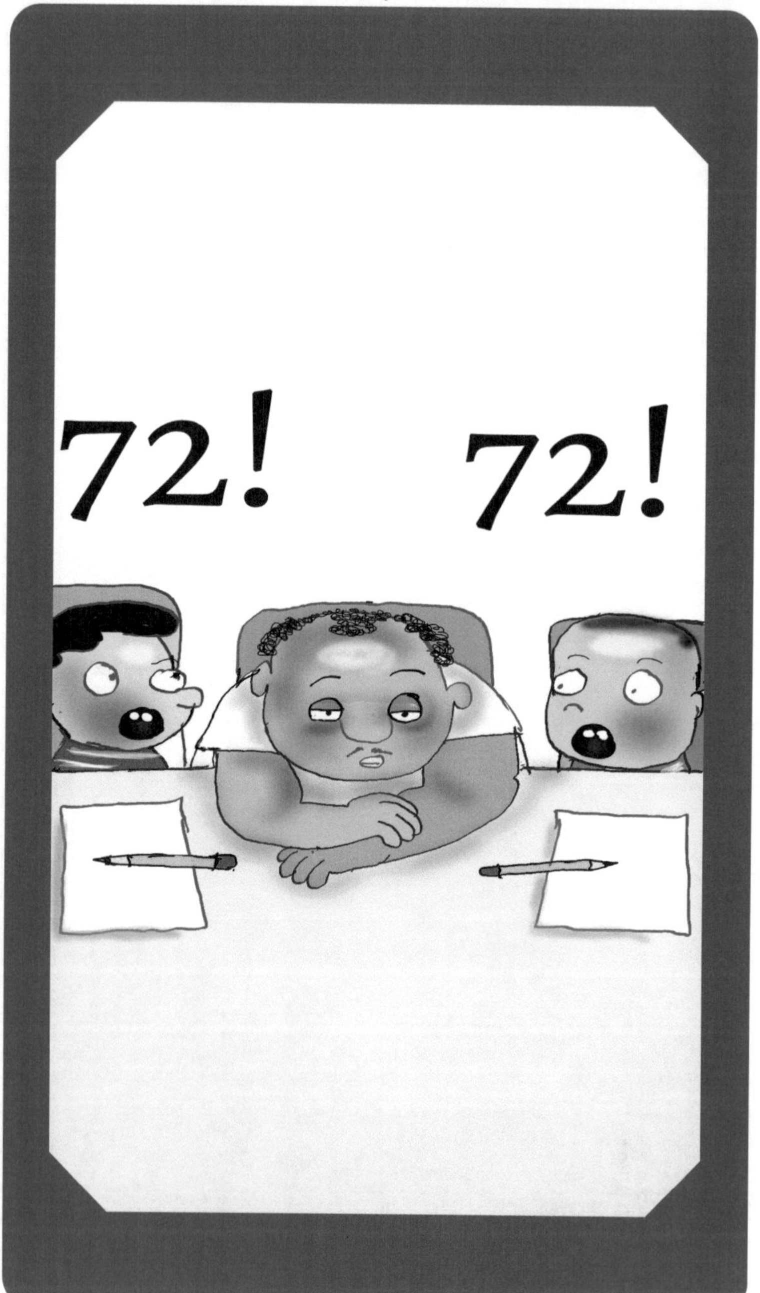
72!
72!

𝒥 used to be quite the prankster. I could sit for hours, waiting to pull off the grandest prank. Slow and steady while executing a prank was the best technique. My favorite prank, the fake mouse prank using Mom's curler and a spool of thread.

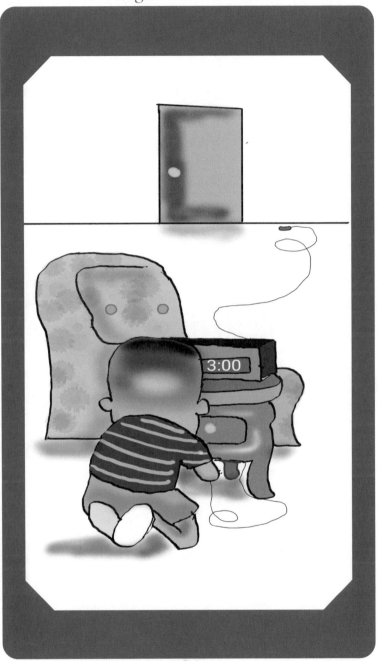

$\mathcal{I}$ was a finicky eater - I'm not gonna lie. I was quite particular about what I digested. Mom was at her wits end, as I was impossible to please. To get through dinners, again I had to adopt the slow and steady approach.

You're always the last one finished....and I'm TIRED of it!

At times, the heat from the Arizona sun was unbearable, too much to withstand when going on a road trip. Thank goodness for the development and creation of modern technology- the automobile air conditioning unit.

Dad....we're burning up back here. We can't feel the air conditioner. You mind turning it up?

While cruising through the neighborhood, Dad pointed to Mom to see the neighbor's brand new Corvette Stingray. Sometimes Mom hears what she wants to hear.

Stingray?

In the driveway?

Can you see his teeth?

Wait. What?

Trick or treat, smell my feet, give me something good to eat! Who remembers that jingle? Halloween was always a blast. Unfortunately, there is an idiot in every crowd who ruins the fun for everybody.

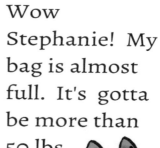

Wow Stephanie! My bag is almost full. It's gotta be more than 50 lbs.

I'm gonna hit a few more houses before I head home. I'll see you there!

Gotta go!
Gotta go!

Shortly after, I visited a particular house with a moron inside. Instead of candy, this jerk passed out ice cubes. Ice cubes, in a paper bag, with heavy candy was bound to be a disaster eventually.

...20
Minutes
Later...

Table tennis matches were vicious. Warren's winning game was based on his wicked serve. Roland won by putting a non returnable spin on the ball. Russell played smash-mouth ping pong, and would win by destroying the other player via brute strength.

My winning style was a bit unorthodox. I won through consistency and tenacity, wearing my opponent down under the winning approach, "Slow and Steady Wins the Race."

Slow and Steady Wins the Race

Next....

Mother knows best, is what they always say. They know how to nurture your body, and limit the intake of sweet treats that are simply bad for you.

Reginald P. Howard

OK... All the pickles,
cucumbers, and tomatoes
are gone, now can I have.....

If you wanted to go to
the pool, somebody
had to spend time with
Stephanie in the shallow
end, so she wouldn't be
left alone, playing by
herself - that was the
rule. I was the designated
'stuckee' every time.

Then there was the time when Dad took us fishing off the pier. The fish seemed to always be lurking just under the pier. It was pretty common to catch a ton of fish by simply dropping the line straight down in the water, vise casting your line far out to catch the big ones. All in all, while out there, "safety" was the word of the day.

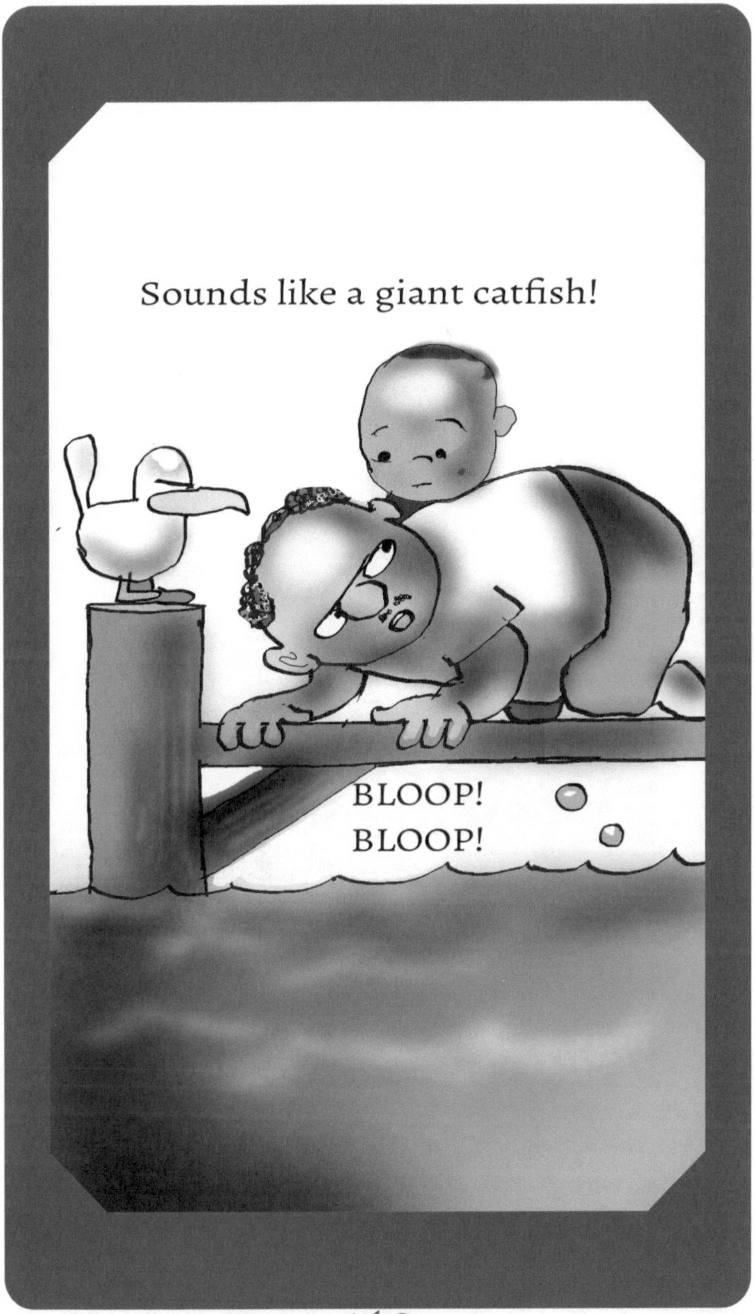
Sounds like a giant catfish!
BLOOP!
BLOOP!

I'm gonna get my pole and catch this sucka, and throw him on the skillet!

Bloop!

Bloop!

What started out as a routine attempt to catch a large fish down below based on sound and movement, turned out to be something more menacing.....

A Manatee!

Slow and Steady Wins the Race

Reginald P. Howard

175

Reginald P. Howard

On yet another car trip into the Arizona mountains, we saw what we called, a Wasp-a-saurus, the largest flying insect we ever saw. This thing flew into an open car window and wreaked havoc immediately.

noun: Waspasaurus - Rex
/Wasp-eh-sor-us/ - /Recs/

A large, six-legged, ferocious, flying menace to society that wreaks havoc and destroys everything in it's path.

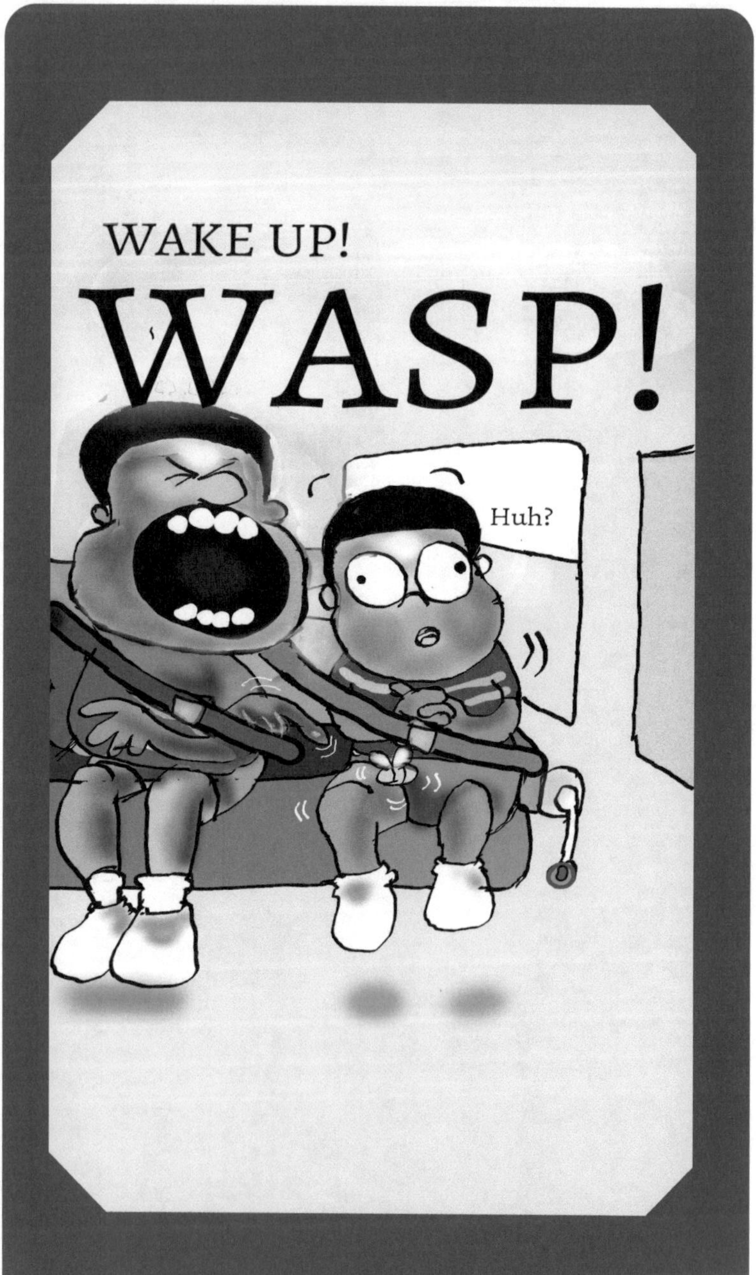
WAKE UP!
WASP!
Huh?

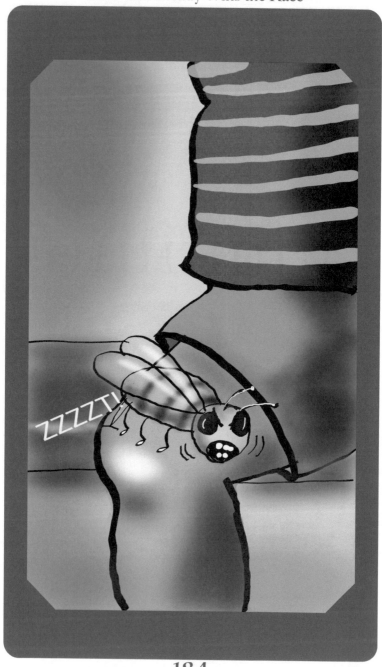

Reginald P. Howard

About this book

Skillful storytelling is both an art and a science. Stories like these, that have been pieced together to form this book, are simply meant to provide entertainment to the reader while maintaining a steady moral compass in the process! These stories feature several hilarious characters, who are members of a real-live African-American family, that spans across their growing years, written and drawn from the perspective of one of the family members. There are tons of other stories to be had, however, this book just captures a small few. The intent here is to be relatable to the lives and home-life of the reader.

Other books by this Author

About the Author and Illustrator

Reginald P. Howard (Reggie) is an award-winning freelance illustrator who has been drawing for the love of art for over 40 years. Born in Amarillo, Texas in 1963, Reginald is the fifth of six siblings. This fun bunch is the offspring of Nona and Olin Howard who still reside in Beavercreek, Ohio today. Aside from a few drawing classes in high school, Reggie's drawing stems from being self-taught and self-refined. Today, he draws with much more purpose and meaning with the publishing of this book and, as an illustrator for a series of children's books that his wife has authored recently.

A graduate of Wright State University, and Averett College for his M.B.A., Reginald works for the federal government in Washington DC and is in the final approach of his career that has lasted over 32 years. But it was the constant, and persistent push from his wife India, who has hinted that his artistic talent is probably something the whole world might want to see. Reggie feels his drawing is a lot like riding a bike; you'll never forget or lose the ability of how to do it once you get started. In fact, according to Reggie, his ability to draw has really refined itself over the years to the point where even he is shocked by what comes out at the end of his pen.

Reggie has drawn freelance for a long time; however, his wife suggested, "instead of just drawing for fun and doodling in your art book, why not package it up in the form of a book for others to see and enjoy?" Why not, he says.

Reggie resides with his wife, and three children, Regan, Daia, and Chancellor, and calls Maryland home. His wife is also a very talented Program Manager who spearheaded the production and release of his books, alongside their daughter Daia, who owns and operates the publishing company who published the professional-quality books that are a class act.

Other books by this Illustrator

Award-Winning Children's Book

The Mice in Paris

A journey of teamwork, victory, and the Olympic spirit
—brace yourself for an unforgettable ride!

COMING SOON

MARCH 2024

Made in the USA
Columbia, SC
08 March 2024

32907169R00104